PAGE 3
PAGE 5
PAGE 6
PAGE 8
PAGE 10
PAGE 11
PAGE 12
PAGE 15
PAGE 17
PAGE 19
PAGE 20
PAGE 21
PAGE 22
PAGE 23
PAGE 27

A E R C N

S V T E P O D R E T

E K P Z 3 9 20 24

PAGE 29
PAGE 31
PAGE 32
PAGE 33

S T M D I U U M E
O T A I E E C E K O

PAGE 35
PAGE 37
PAGE 38

B N R X

PAGE 39

5 10 16 22

PAGE 40
PAGE 41
PAGE 42

THESE STICKERS ARE JUST FOR FUN!

TRANSFORMERS
ROBOTS IN DISGUISE

1001 STICKERS

COLOUR OPTIMUS PRIME

Optimus Prime has summoned Bumblebee to assemble a new team of Autobots. A Decepticon army is planning to invade Earth, and the Autobots must protect it. Colour the picture.

WHICH BOT SAID WHAT?

Bumblebee's new recruits are young and inexperienced but they must learn to work together as a team. Place the stickers to finish the Bots. Look at the clues for each one to work out who said what.

BUMBLEBEE
Optimistic
Adventurous
Driven

I AM BUILT FOR THE TOUGH STUFF! OOPS! I FELL OVER!

a

SIDESWIPE
Street-smart
Rebellious
Quick

ROLL OUT, TEAM! WE WILL COMPLETE THIS MISSION.

B

GRIMLOCK
Strong
Hulking
Clumsy

I THINK WE SHOULD TAKE A DIFFERENT ROUTE. IT WILL BE QUICKER!

C

STRONGARM
Loyal
Stubborn
Follows the rules

I WILL NOT LEAVE YOU, BUMBLEBEE. SERVE AND PROTECT!

D

MEMORY MISSION

Can you complete this mind-bending memory mission? Study the picture below for one minute. Then cover it up and answer the questions at the bottom of the page.

1 How many characters are in the scene?

2 Who is Fixit, the orange repair robot, standing nearest to?

3 What animal is in the background wearing a hat?

4 How many Decepticons are in the picture?

5 Which Autobot is running?

6 Is Optimus Prime in the scene?

BUMBLEBEE'S COOL RIDE

The leader of the new Autobot team is always ready to roll out in his alt-mode vehicle – a cool yellow sports car. Place the missing stickers to complete Bumblebee's awesome ride.

IT'S TIME TO PUT THE PEDAL DOWN AND ROLL OUT!

ROLL AND REPAIR

One of the Autobots needs an urgent repair. Luckily, Fixit is always on hand with the right tools for the job. Add stickers to complete Fixit, then follow the lines to lead the right Autobot in for repair.

GRIMLOCK

STRONGARM

BUMBLEBEE

SIDESWIPE

FIXIT

ODD BOT OUT

New Autobot recruits need sharp observational skills and an eye for detail. Only one of the Bots below is the real Sideswipe, but can you spot which one? Use the big picture as a guide.

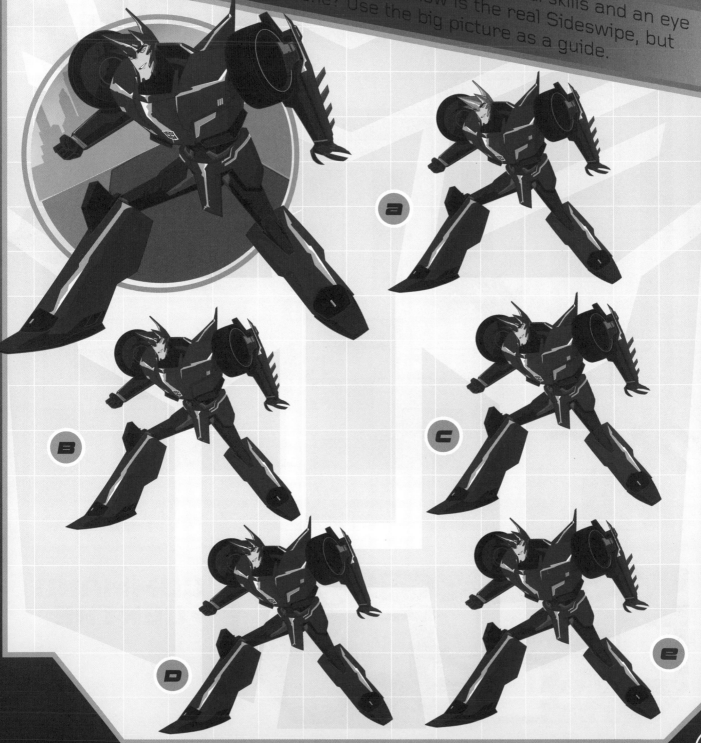

NAVIGATE MISSION

Decepticons are invading the Command Centre! Place the stickers to finish the picture below, then help Bumblebee find a safe route through the city streets to the Command Centre as fast as you can!

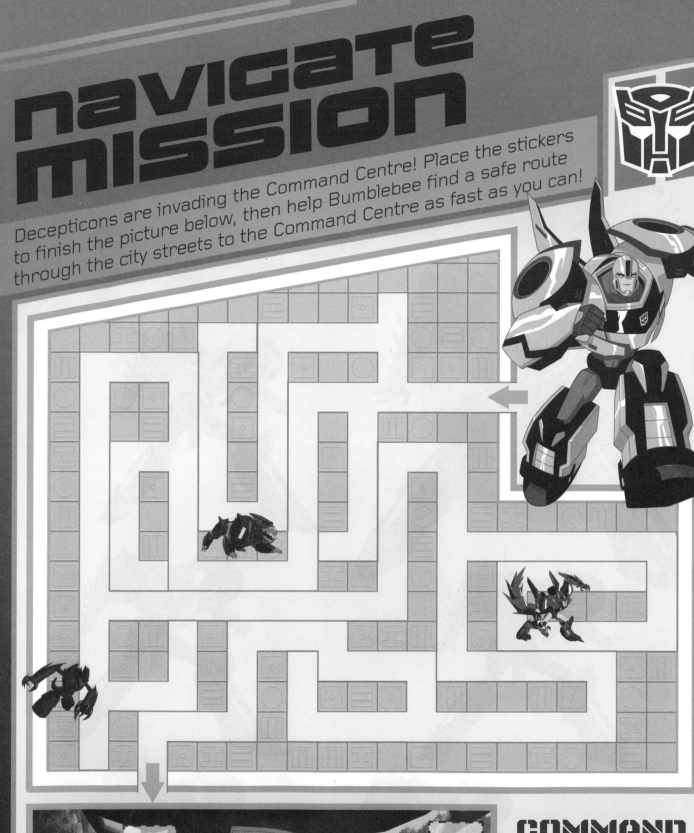

COMMAND CENTRE

COLOUR SIDESWIPE

Sideswipe is quick on his feet... and wheels! This bright-red Bot thinks fast, and moves even faster! He's all about defeating the Decepticons, and looking good doing it. Colour the picture.

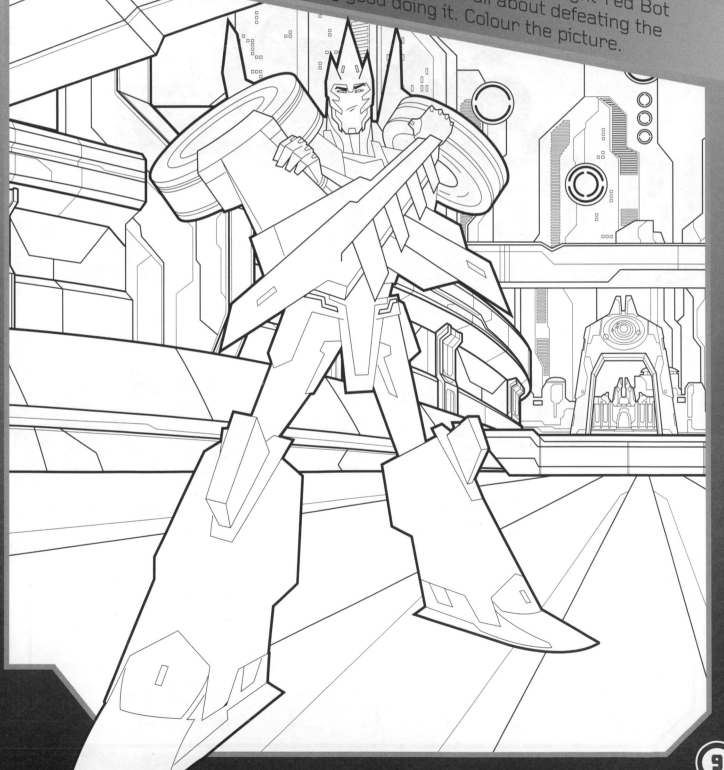

MESSAGE MIX-UP

Can you crack Optimus Prime's scrambled message to Bumblebee? Identify the letters that appear twice in each box, then place the correct stickers in the numbered boxes to reveal the message.

1 S G Z B C A S

2 E G O E C N K

3 R A M R T J I

4 X V J E R V O

5 E H L E U S G

6 A R Y A F K M

7 N U S A E T N

8 D H D L U S G

9 E L Y P C P I

10 D B R E Z T R

11 O H L U O S G

12 T H L U T S G

13 E H E L U S G

14 C H L C U S G

15 T H L U T S G

1 2 3 4 5   6 7 8

9 10 11 12 13 14 15

STICKER PICTURE GRIMLOCK

Grimlock is a huge, hulking Tyrannosaurus Rex Dinobot – in fact, he's the strongest Autobot in the team. This Bot fights hard and plays hard! Find the missing stickers to complete this picture.

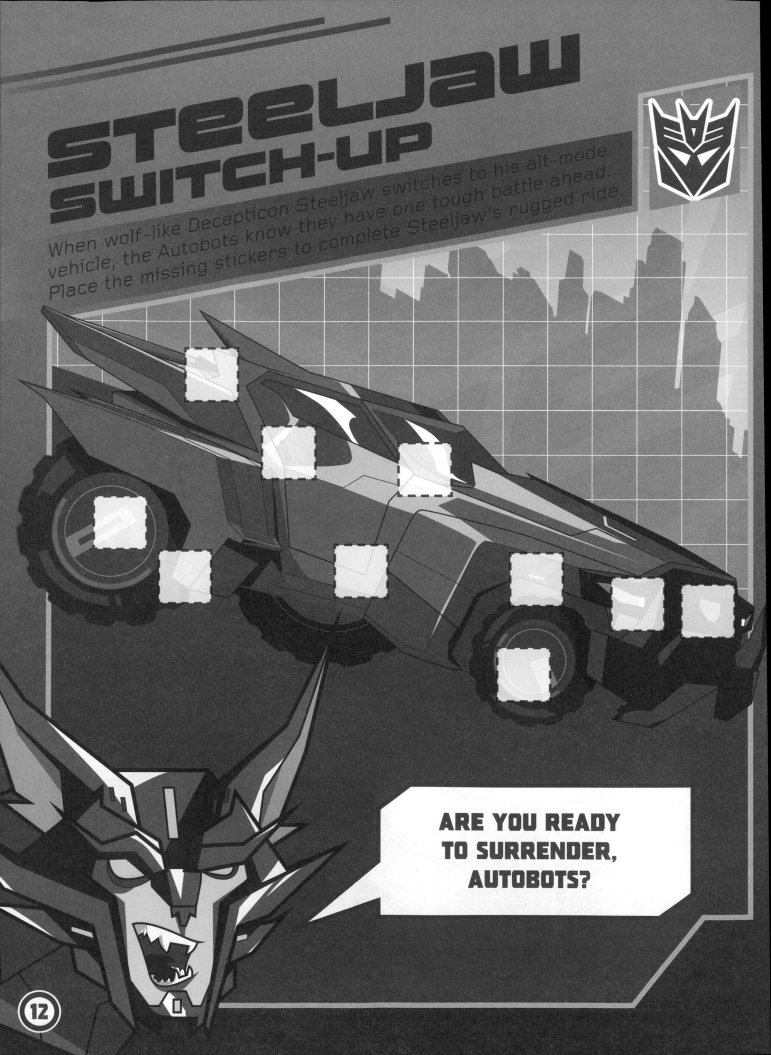

WHAT'S NOT RIGHT?

Take a close look at this city park scene – things are not quite as they seem. Can you identify and circle 10 things that are not right about the picture?

ODD BOT OUT

Have you got what it takes to identify the genuine Autobot amongst the imitators? Only one Autobot below is the real Strongarm. Using the big picture as a guide, can you spot which one?

a

B

C

D

e

MISSION DECODE

The Autobots have received an emergency message but it's in code. Find the stickers to complete the Code Index. Then use it to decipher the message. What's the emergency?

CODE INDEX

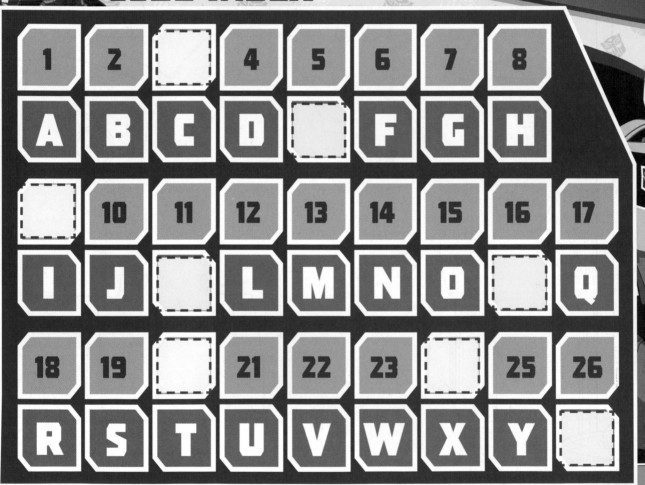

8-21-14-4-18-5-4-19   15-6

_ _ _ _ _ _ _ _   _ _

4-5-3-5-16-20-9-3-15-14-19   1-18-5

_ _ _ _ _ _ _ _ _ _ _   _ _ _

12-15-15-19-5   15-14   5-1-18-20-8!

_ _ _ _ _   _ _   _ _ _ _ _!

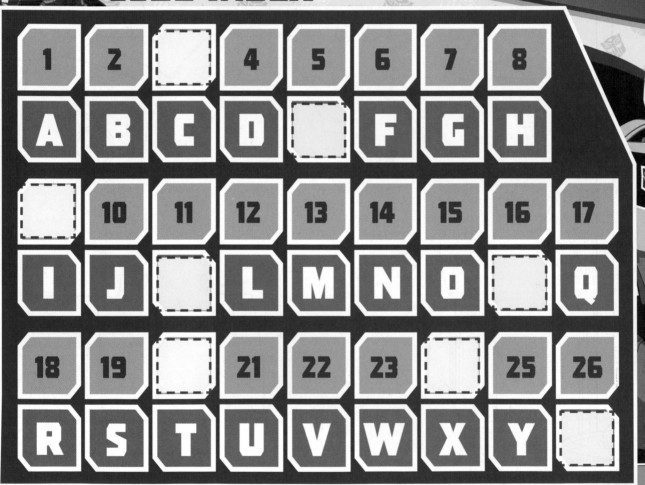

15

COLOUR BUMBLEBEE

The yellow and black Autobot, Bumblebee, is a busy Bot! He has a boundless optimism and taste for adventure and this heroic leader is always ready to roll out! Colour the picture.

MISSION TO WHERE?

Where is each Autobot's emergency mission destination? Read the clues and then use your stickers to put each Autobot in the correct location.

> SO MANY RUSTY OLD CARS EVERYWHERE!

> I HOPE I DON'T GET SEASICK ON THIS MISSION!

> WHAT IS THIS PLACE? THE MIDDLE OF NOWHERE?

> IT'S A BUSY PLACE. I NEED TO MAKE SURE I STAY IN ALT-MODE!

a SCRAPYARD

B SHIP DECK

C CITY

D COUNTRYSIDE

SHADOW MATCH

Fixit is the hyperactive Mini-Con that every robot needs around. He's a mechanical genius who can fix anything that bleeps and blips. Look at the shadows. Which one matches Fixit exactly?

STICKER PICTURE OPTIMUS PRIME

Optimus Prime handed leadership of the next team of Autobots over to Bumblebee, the only Bot he trusts with this responsibility. Place the missing stickers to complete Optimus Prime.

19

AUTOBOT BASICS

Bumblebee and his team of Autobots are all different in their own ways. Place the missing stickers, then draw lines to match the Autobots to their correct descriptions.

B A BOT WITH A BIG HEART, HE FIGHTS HARD AND PLAYS HARD.

a HYPERACTIVE BOT THAT CAN FIX ANY ROBOT ERROR.

a PROTECTIVE OF THE AUTOBOTS AND GIVES GUIDANCE TO THEM.

D QUICK WITH HIS WORDS AND HANDS.

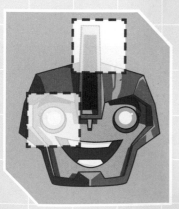

e LOVES ADVENTURE AND IS ALWAYS OPTIMISTIC.

F DEDICATED TO ENFORCING THE LAW, NO MATTER WHAT.

CAR CHASE

Sideswipe needs to be reunited with his red alt-mode supercar. Place the stickers to complete the picture, then find a route through the city park maze as fast as you can!

PUZZLE MISSION

This is a mega sticker mission! Find and place the 10 missing stickers for each picture puzzle to reveal four awesome Autobot mission images.

SIDESWIPE'S WHEELS

Red Autobot Sideswipe is always ready to roll out with the team. Like Bumblebee, His alt-mode is a luxury sports car. Place the missing stickers to complete Sideswipe's ride.

ONE TEAM, ONE MISSION. BUMBLEBEE, LET'S ROLL OUT!

HIDING OUT

Bumblebee and the Autobot team love to play tricks – when there's not an emergency to attend to, that is. They are hiding from Fixit somewhere in this scene. Can you find all five Bots?

ODD BOT OUT

Can you spot the real T-Rex Autobot Grimlock amongst the rogue Dinobots below? Using the big picture as a guide, look closely and find the bona fide Bot!

a

b

c

d

e

COLOUR STRONGARM

Strongarm is a loyal member of the Autobot team. Single-minded and dedicated, this law-abiding Bot always delivers when it matters! Colour in the picture.

GRIDLOCK

Place the stickers to complete the picture puzzles. There can only be one of each Autobot in each column, row and two-by-two square. Watch out, each one gets trickier!

1

2

3

4

AUTOBOT WORD SEARCH

Here's another Autobot brain-buster! Search out all the Bot related words in the grid below. Words can be read up, down, forwards, backwards and diagonally.

A	T	R	A	M	Z	T	Y	G	N	O	I	S	S	I	M
G	R	O	P	T	I	M	U	S	H	Y	K	C	D	T	E
K	A	X	A	W	C	R	U	E	W	C	B	T	C	Q	P
P	N	T	J	U	N	K	T	C	O	L	V	N	O	M	I
Z	S	Q	P	Z	T	U	O	L	L	O	R	R	P	V	W
Z	F	X	S	B	U	O	M	O	K	R	E	N	B	K	S
L	O	U	E	K	V	I	B	U	M	B	L	E	B	E	E
C	R	U	P	Y	R	J	K	O	B	Q	J	C	F	B	D
P	M	I	O	G	R	R	O	A	T	P	R	C	S	L	I
Y	E	D	E	C	E	P	T	I	C	O	N	W	P	R	S
R	R	W	Y	R	O	L	M	N	B	T	P	U	K	J	H
T	S	I	O	E	U	C	M	R	A	G	N	O	R	T	S

BUMBLEBEE	**AUTOBOT**	**ROLL OUT**
SIDESWIPE	**DECEPTICON**	**MISSION**
STRONGARM	**OPTIMUS**	
GRIMLOCK	**TRANFORMERS**	

STICKER PICTURE BUMBLEBEE

Bumblebee loves a challenge, and takes leadership of the Autobots very seriously. With each mission he is becoming a stronger leader. Place the missing stickers to complete Bumblebee's transformation.

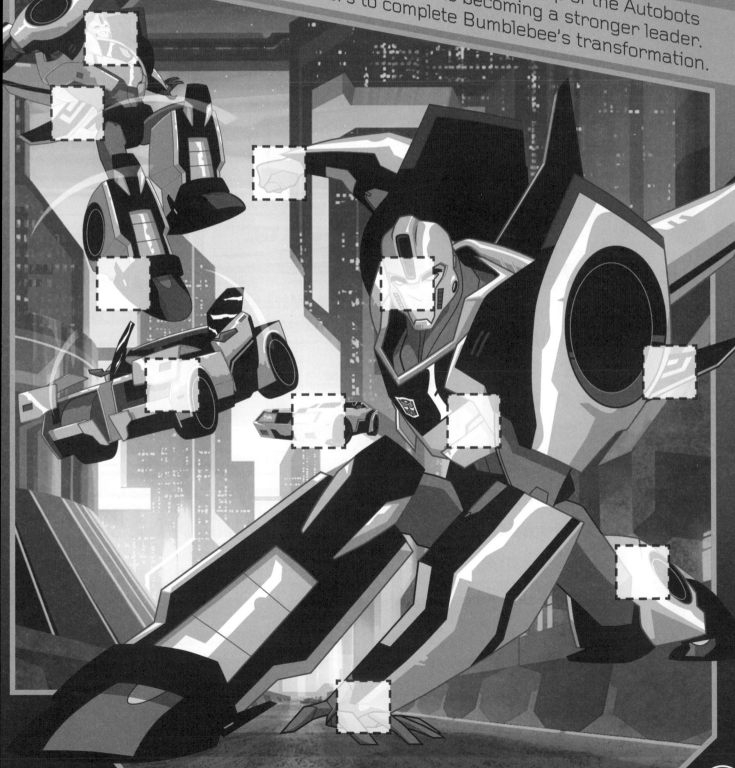

AUTOBOT REVISION

Think you know everything about the Robots in Disguise? It's time to test your Autobot brain! Choose from the words below and write them in to finish the facts.

1 BUMBLEBEE IS A BRIGHT .... AND BLACK AUTOBOT.

2 DENNY RUNS A .... WHICH IS FULL OF RUSTY OLD CARS.

3 .... IS THE LEADER OF THE AUTOBOTS, AND OPTIMUS PRIME .... THEM ON THEIR MISSIONS.

4 SIDESWIPE IS THE .... AUTOBOT ON WHEELS.

5 STRONGARM ALWAYS FOLLOWS THE .... OF THE LAW.

6 GRIMLOCK'S ALT-MODE IS A T-REX ....

7 A DECEPTICON .... HAS CRASH-LANDED ON PLANET EARTH.

8 BUMBLEBEE IS DETERMINED TO FILL OPTIMUS PRIME'S SHOES AS THE ....

LETTER	DINOBOT	TEAM LEADER
BUMBLEBEE	SCRAPYARD	YELLOW
GUIDES	FASTEST	SPACESHIP

COMPLETE THE SEQUENCES

Can you think as fast as Sideswipe? Look at the sequences below and see if you can spot the patterns. Place the stickers in the correct boxes to complete the line-ups correctly.

        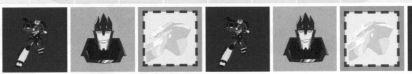

31

STRONGARM'S MOTOR

Strongarm's sense of justice is second to none, and when things heat up she's a zero-tolerance crime-fighting machine! Place the missing stickers to complete Strongarm's police SUV alt-mode.

DECEPTICONS ON THE LOOSE? NOT ON MY WATCH!

CROSSWORD

Can you solve this Autobot crossword? Look at the clues and place the stickers of the letters on the grid. Write in the remaining letters when you have worked out the words.

1 _ U T O _ **2**

4 S T

5

3 _ I D E

A

CLUES

1. A___BOT
2. B__BLEB__
3. S___SWIP_
4. __E_LJ_W
5. GR__L___

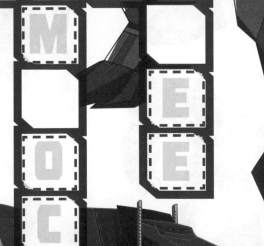

ODD BOT OUT

Even Optimus Prime isn't free from copycats! Only one of the pictures below is the genuine legendary Autobot leader, Optimus Prime. Using the big picture as a guide, can you spot which one?

a

B

c

D

E

STICKER PICTURE
SIDESWIPE

A rebel and a lone wolf, Sideswipe looks out for himself first and wishes Strongarm would cut him a break with all her rules and regulations! Place the missing stickers to complete this picture.

COLOUR GRIMLOCK

Mean, green T-Rex Grimlock is the strongest of the Autobots – you don't want to get in this robot's way when he's on the rampage! Colour the roarsome picture.

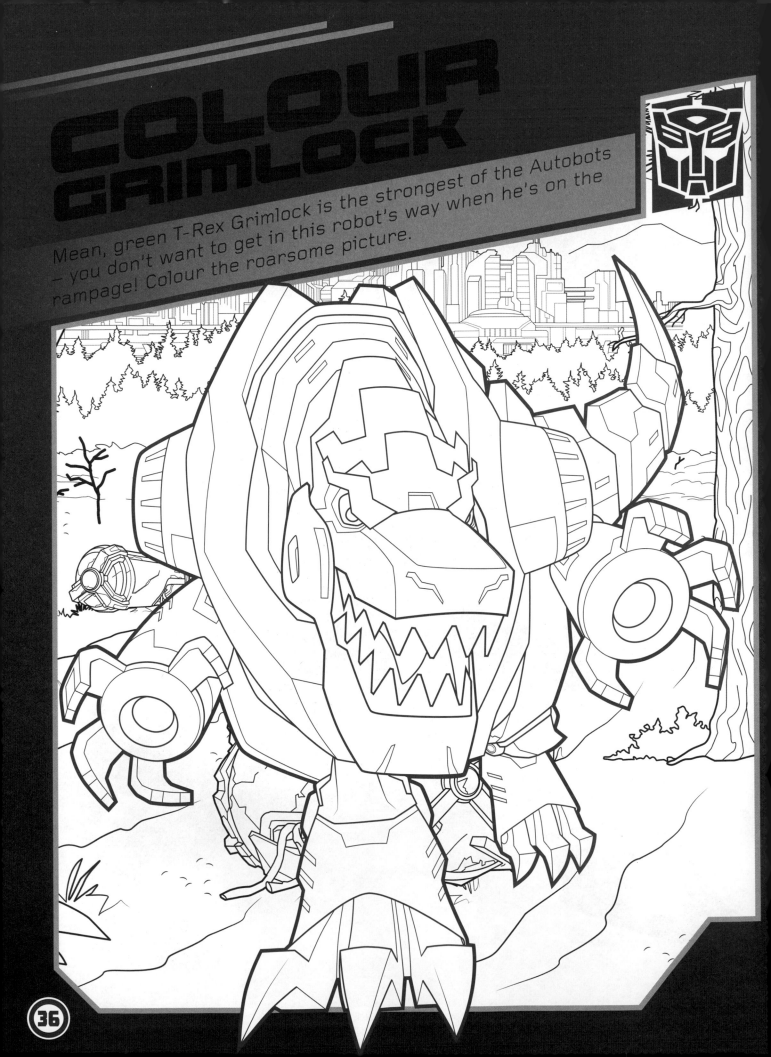

CAPTURE STEELJAW

The Autobots must race to recapture Steeljaw before he escapes from his stasis pod prison! Add the missing stickers, then help the Autobots find a route through the maze.

CODE BREAKER

Bumblebee has sent a message to the Autobots, but his radio has scrambled it. Find the stickers to complete the Code Index. Then use it to decipher the message and write it below.

CODE INDEX

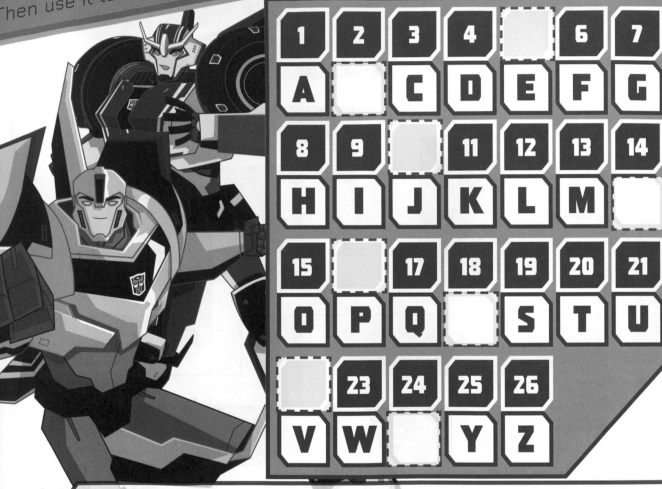

1	2	3	4		6	7
A		C	D	E	F	G

8	9		11	12	13	14
H	I	J	K	L	M	

15		17	18	19	20	21
O	P	Q		S	T	U

	23	24	25	26
V	W		Y	Z

12-5-20'19   18-15-12-12   15-21-20   1-14-4

_ _ _'_ _ _ _ _ _ _ _ _ _ _,

18-5-3-1-16-20-21-18-5   20-8-15-19-5

_ _ _ _ _ _ _ _ _ _ _ _ _ _

4-5-3-5-16-20-9-3-15-14-19!

_ _ _ _ _ _ _ _ _ _ _!

PUZZLE MISSION

The Autobots never know where their next mission will take them, but they love fighting crime and keeping people safe wherever they are. Find the stickers to complete these four picture puzzles.

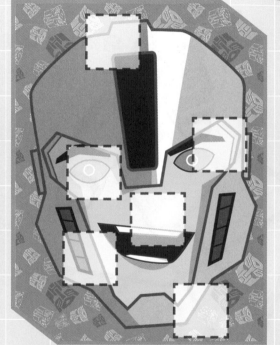

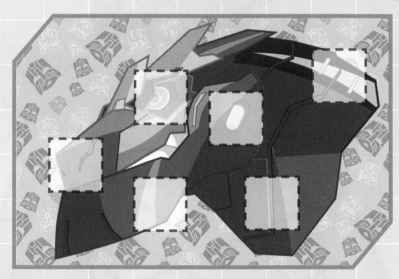

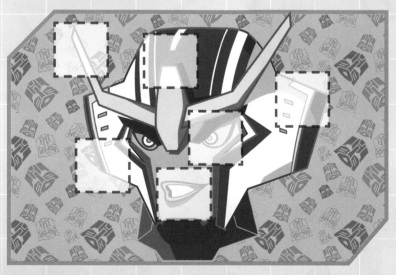

CALL TO DUTY

Grimlock and Strongarm need to reach the other Bots to roll out on their next mission. Add stickers to complete the picture. Then follow the lines to reveal which Bot reaches them in time.

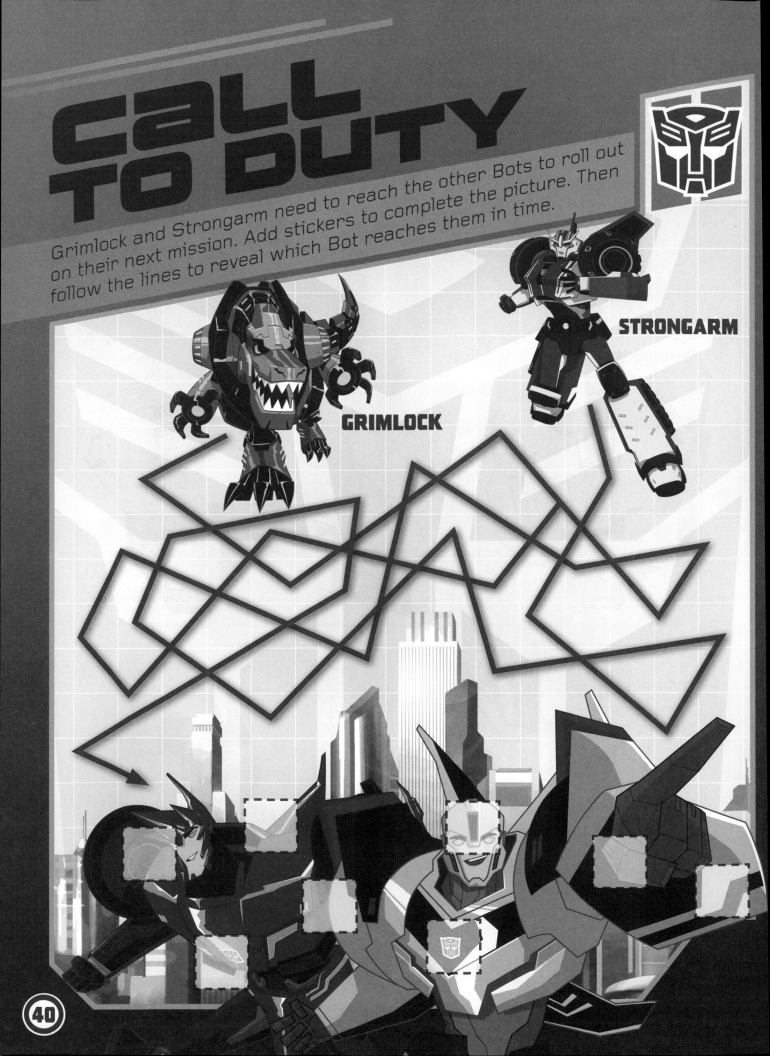

GRIMLOCK

STRONGARM

STICKER PICTURE
BAD BOTS

Steeljaw is a born leader and is always hatching a terrible plan to take over planet Earth. Use the stickers to finish this picture of Steeljaw and his Decepticon army.

OPTIMUS PRIME'S TRUCK

Optimus Prime is the ultimate protector and advisor for the Autobot team. Place the stickers to complete Optimus Prime's awesome alt-mode truck.

OPTIMUS PRIME HERE.
IT'S AN HONOUR
SERVING WITH YOU,
AUTOBOTS.

ROBOT ROUND-UP

There's a lot of Bots on this page and they need rounding up. Use your sharp sight to count the pictures, then write your answers in the boxes.

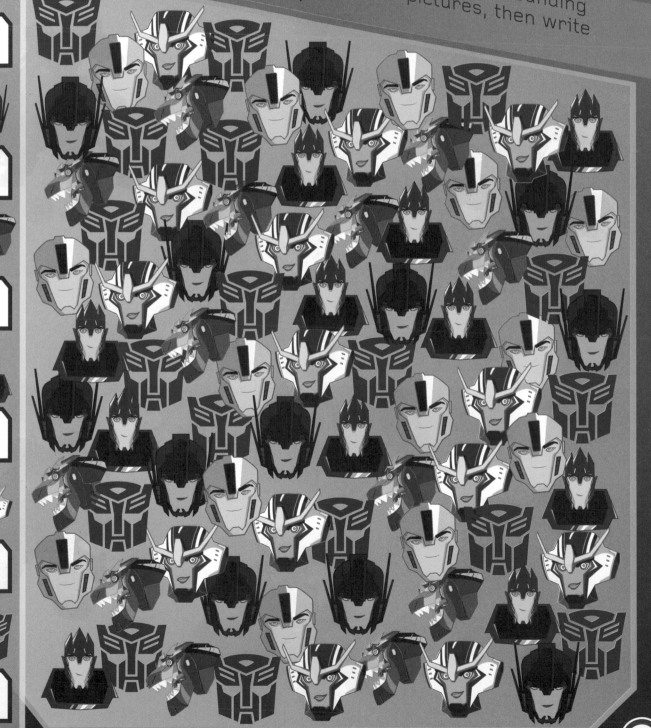

SHADOW MATCH

There is only one team of awesome Autobots on planet Earth! Look closely at the shadows below. Can you spot which one matches the team picture exactly?

a

b

c

d

e

STICKER PICTURE STRONGARM

Strongarm is getting ready to roll out and recapture some Decepticon criminals. Place the stickers to complete this picture of Strongarm and make sure she's ready for action!

ROBOTS IN DISGUISE

Under Bumblebee's leadership, the Autobots are learning to work together as one mean team machine. It's time to roll out, Autobots! Colour the picture.